I-SPY

Z
WILDLIFE

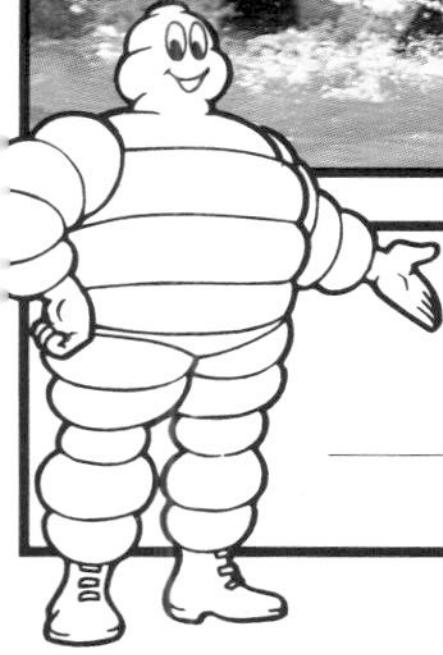

This I-Spy book belongs to:

____

Aardvark
What is the other, common, name for this odd animal?
Spy scores ***10***

Addax
The Addax lives in deserts and never needs to drink. True or False?
Spy scores ***10***

Alligator

This is the Chinese Alligator. A crocodile's front two teeth can be seen when its mouth is closed whereas an alligator's can not. True or False?

Spy scores ***5***

Anteater

What does the Giant Anteater use to trap ants and termites?

Spy scores ***10***

Antelope

The Roan Antelope lives in southern Africa but its name suggests it resembles a more familar animal. Which?

Spy scores ***5***

Armadillo

Armadillos are found only on one continent. Which one? The animal in this picture is a Hairy Armadillo.

Spy scores ***10***

Barbet
This is the Gaudy Barbet. There are at least eighty other kinds of these brightly coloured birds. True or False?
Spy scores ***10***

Basilisk
What is unusual about the way in which the Plumed Basilisk Lizard runs?
Spy scores ***10***

Bear
What is the Brown Bear often called in North America?
Spy scores ***5***

Polar Bear
Polar Bears hate water. True or False?
Spy scores ***5***

Beetle

How does the Rhinoceros Scarab Beetle get its name?
Spy scores ***15***

Bison

Bison are correctly called buffaloes. True or False?
Spy scores ***5***

Bluebird

Like many hummingbirds, the Fairy Bluebird eats mainly one kind of food. Which?
Spy scores ***10***

Answer the question to double your score!

Boar

Wild Boars are closely related to farm pigs. True or False?
*Spy scores **5***

Bushbaby

At what time of the day do bushbabies look for food?
*Spy scores **15***

Camel
The single-humped Arabian Camel has another name. What is it?
*Spy scores **5***

Camel
Where does the two-humped Bactrian Camel come from?
*Spy scores **5***

Chamaeleon

The three horns identify this as a male Jackson's Chamaeleon. Chamaeleons can point one eye forwards and one back at the same time. True or False?
*Spy scores **5***

Cheetah

The Cheetah can run at speeds of more than 160 km/h (100 mph). True or False?
*Spy scores **5***

Chimpanzee

Chimpanzees are thought to be our closest living relatives. True or False.

*Spy scores **5***

Cobra

An Indian Cobra can spit poison to defend itself. True or False?

*Spy scores **10***

Cockatoo

What feature distinguishes cockatoos from most other kinds of parrots? This is a Roseate Cockatoo.
*Spy scores **5***

Coral-fish

This coral fish gets its name from the shape of its tail which is also similar to the shape of the Bongo's horns. What is its name?
*Spy scores **10***

Crab

Why is the Hermit Crab so called?
*Spy scores **10***

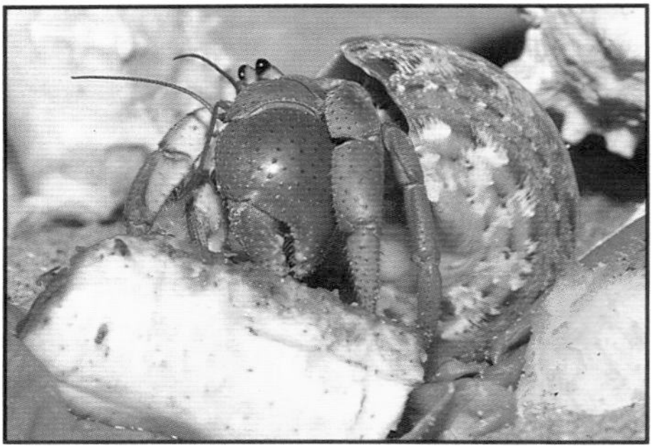

Crocodile
How can you tell a male crocodile from a female?
*Spy scores **10***

Cuttlefish
Like chamaeleons, cuttlefishes are able to change colour to match their surroundings. True or False?
*Spy scores **15***

Deer

This is a Swamp Deer. All male deer have antlers. True or False?

Spy scores ***5***

Dolphin

To which other kind of fish is the dolphin related?

Spy scores ***5***

Dragon

This is a Bearded Dragon. What part of the world does this lizard come from?
*Spy scores **15***

Dragon-fish

Also called the Lion-fish, why are its spines so very dangerous?
*Spy scores **15***

Answer the question to double your score!

Eagle
This is the Short-toed Eagle. Do you know what its favourite food is?
*Spy scores **10***

Eel
The Conger Eel can reach almost 3 metres (9 feet) in length. True or False?
*Spy scores **15***

African Elephant

The African Elephant has smaller ears than its Asian cousin. True or False?

*Spy scores **5***

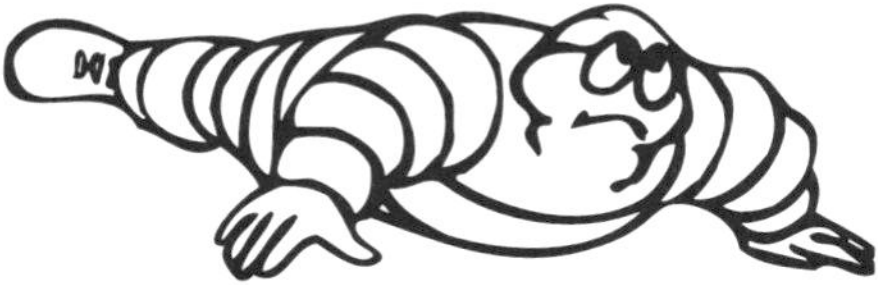

Indian Elephant

Female Indian Elephants have larger tusks than males. True or False?

*Spy scores **5***

Emu

There is only one other kind of bird which is bigger than the Australian Emu. It is also flightless. Which bird is it?
*Spy scores **5***

Flamingo

How do flamingoes feed?
*Spy scores **5***

Fox

This is a Fennec Fox. Its large eyes and huge ears are clues to the time of day the animal is active. When?
*Spy scores **15***

Frog

Why is the Poison-arrow Frog so brightly coloured.
*Spy scores **15***

Answer the question to double your score!

Gazelle
Where do Thomson's Gazelles live?
Spy scores ***5***

Gecko
Some geckoes can walk upside-down on the ceiling of a room. True or False?
Spy scores ***10***

Gemsbok
To which other animal shown in this book is this antelope closely related?
Spy scores ***10***

Gibbon
How does the Lar Gibbon move among the trees?
Spy scores ***10***

Giraffe

How many bones does a Giraffe have in its long neck.
*Spy scores **5***

Gorilla

What nickname is often given to an adult male Gorilla owing to the colour of part of his coat?
*Spy scores **5***

Hippopotamus
What does the name of this animal mean?
Spy scores ***5***

Hornbill
The Hornbill's beak is very heavy. True or False?
Spy scores ***10***

Horse

Przewalski's Wild Horse is now very rare in the wild. Where does it come from?

Spy scores ***10***

Ibis

The long legs and bill of the Scarlet Ibis are clues to the habitat in which it lives. What is it?

Spy scores ***5***

Iguana
The Common Iguana is a good swimmer. True or False?
*Spy scores **5***

Jaguar
Which wild South American cat is bigger than the Jaguar?
*Spy scores **10***

Kangaroo
This is a Big Red. What is the name given to the group of animals to which the Kangaroo belongs?
Spy scores ***5***

Kiwi
How fast can a New Zealand Kiwi fly?
Spy scores ***15***

Koala
The Koala is a kind of bear. True or False?
Spy scores ***10***

Kookaburra

Because of its call, what is the common name sometimes given to this Australian bird?
Spy scores ***10***

Lemur

Lemurs are found mainly on one large island off the coast of East Africa. Which? This is a Ruffed Lemur.
Spy scores ***15***

Answer the question to double your score!

Leopard
Where do Leopards sometimes store their kills for safety?
Spy scores ***10***

Lion
Lions live mainly in dense jungle. True or False?
Spy scores ***5***

Llama
From which wild South American animal is the domestic Llama bred?
*Spy scores **5***

Locust
To which well-known insects are locusts related?
*Spy scores **5***

Loris

To which group of animals, that also includes monkeys, apes, and humans, does the Loris belong? This is a Slender Loris.
Spy scores ***15***

Lynx

The Caracal Lynx is a member of the Dog family. True or False?
Spy scores ***10***

Macaw

From which subcontinent does the Scarlet Macaw come?

*Spy scores **5***

Mandrill

In what kind of habitat do Mandrills normally live?

*Spy scores **15***

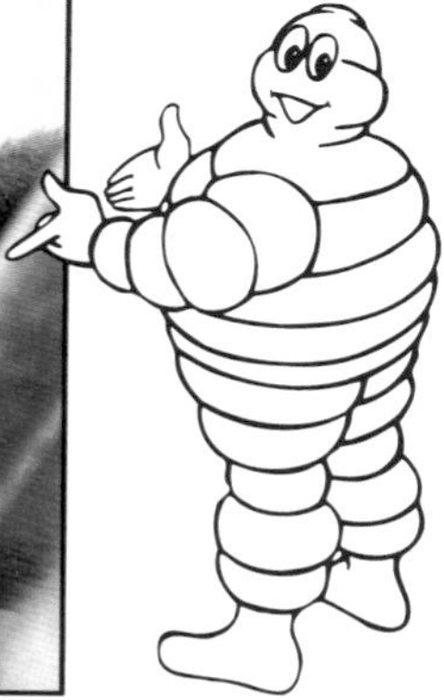

Marmoset

A Marmoset's hand is different from that of most other monkeys and apes in one important way. What is it?
*Spy scores **10***

Meerkat

Meerkats are members of the Cat family. True or False?
*Spy scores **10***

Mongoose

What is the plural of the word 'Mongoose'?
*Spy scores **10***

Monkey

This is a Black-and-white Colobus Monkey. Which continent does it come from?
Spy scores ***5***

Muskox

How do Muskoxen defend themselves against attack from wolves?
Spy scores ***5***

Answer the question to double your score!

Ocelot

Why have Ocelots become so rare?
Spy scores ***15***

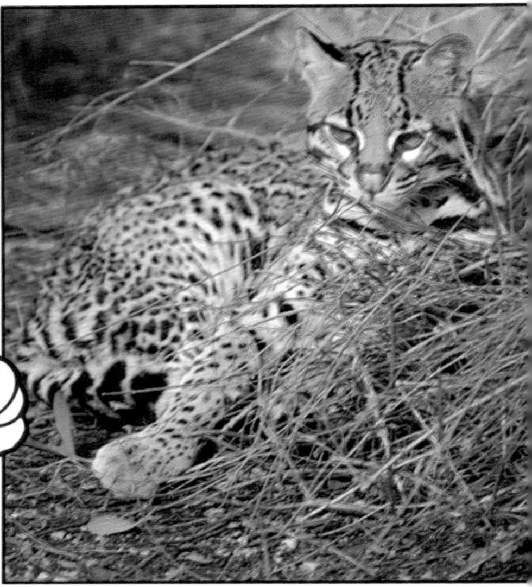

Okapi

To which other long-necked animal is the Okapi related?
Spy scores ***10***

Orang-utan

One of every zoo's favourite great apes, the Orang-utan comes from Borneo but do you know what its name means?

*Spy scores **5***

Oryx

Rare or perhaps extinct in the wild, where does this beautiful animal come from?

*Spy scores **15***

Ostrich

A single egg of this unmistakable bird is as big as forty hen's eggs. True or False?
Spy scores ***5***

Otter

Otters are closely related to badgers. True or False?
Spy scores ***15***

Owl
This is an Eagle Owl. Can owls see in total darkness?
*Spy scores **10***

Panda
The Giant Panda has been adopted as a symbol for endangered wildlife. It eats only one kind of food — what?
*Spy scores **5***

Answer the question to double your score!

Penguin
This is a King Penguin which comes from Antarctica. Do you know how many eggs the female lays?
Spy scores ***5***

Piranha
These small to medium-sized fish live in the rivers of South America. They will attack only if there are more than 20 piranhas in a shoal: True or False?
Spy scores ***10***

Porcupine
If attacked, a Crested Porcupine will charge backwards at its enemy. True or False?
Spy scores ***10***

Possum
What word is used to describe the tail of an animal like Leadbeater's Possum which uses it to help it climb among trees.
Spy scores ***10***

Praying Mantis
The Praying Mantis eats mainly other insects, and a female will even eat her mate if he is not careful. But do you know how it gets its name?
Spy scores ***10***

Python

This is a Royal Python. A python can survive for up to twelve months without eating. True or False?

*Spy scores **10***

Reindeer

What is the other name for a Reindeer?

*Spy scores **10***

Rhea

The Rhea from South America is the heaviest bird capable of flying. True or False?

*Spy scores **10***

Rhinoceros
Black Rhinos are now very rare because poachers hunt them for their horns. What is the horn made of?
Spy scores ***10***

Seahorse
A seahorse is a sea-dwelling mammal. True or False?
Spy scores ***15***

Sealion

The breeding site of a Sealion is called a rookery. True or False?

Spy scores ***5***

Serval

How many animals live in a group of Servals?

Spy scores ***15***

Shark

This is a Black-finned Reef Shark. What is the spine of a shark made of?

Spy scores ***10***

Snake

This is a Mexican Milk Snake. Why are some snakes so boldly coloured?
Spy scores ***10***

Spider

This is a so-called Bird-eating Spider. Which continent do these spiders come from?
Spy scores ***15***

Swan
This is a Black Swan. Where do Black Swans come from?
*Spy scores **5***

Tamarin
This is a Golden Lion Tamarin. How does this little primate get its name?
*Spy scores **15***

Tapir
The Brazilian Tapir is an excellent swimmer. True or False?
*Spy scores **10***

Terrapin
Box Terrapins occasionally enter water; are they amphibians or reptiles?
Spy scores ***10***

Tiger
Lions are bigger than Tigers. True or False?
Spy scores ***5***

Toucan

Toucans are very bold birds and, in the wild, will even come into houses. What do they eat?

Spy scores ***10***

Vicuna

This animal is the wild form of an animal that you have already seen in this book. Which one?

Spy scores ***15***

Wolf

To which family of animals does the Wolf belong?
Spy scores ***5***

Zebra

Zebra's are among a zoo's best-known animals but why are they striped?
Spy scores ***5***

INDEX

Answers

Aardvark: Earth-pig
Addax: True.
Alligator: True
Anteater: Its sticky tongue.
Antelope: Horse.
Armadillo: America.
Barbet: True.
Basilisk: It runs on two legs
Bear: Grizzly Bear.
Polar Bear: False.
Beetle: From the horn-like projection on the front of its head.
Bison: False.
Bluebird: Nectar.
Boar: True.
Bushbaby: At night.
Camel: Dromedary.
Camel: Central Asia, China, and Mongolia.
Chamaeleon: True.
Cheetah: False).
Chimpanzee: True.
Cobra: True.
Cockatoo: The crest on its head which the bird can raise when alarmed.
Coral-fish: Lyre-tail Coral-fish.
Crab: Because it occupies the empty shells of other sea creatures.
Crocodile: It is almost impossible to tell males from females.
Cuttlefish: True.
Deer: False.
Dolphin: Dolphins are mammals.
Dragon: Australia.
Dragon-fish: They contain a deadly poison.
Eagle: Snakes and other reptiles.
Eel: True.
African Elephant: False.
Indian Elephant: False.
Emu: Ostrich.
Flamingo: By filtering food particles from the water.
Fox: At night.
Frog: To warn enemies that it is poisonous.
Gazelle: East African grasslands.
Gecko: True.
Gemsbok: Roan Antelope.
Gibbon: By swinging from branches or by running along them.
Giraffe: Seven, the same number as a human.
Gorilla: Silverback.
Hippopotamus: River horse.
Hornbill: False. It is a light, honeycombed material.
Horse: Mongolia and western China.
Ibis: Wetland.
Iguana: True.
Jaguar: None. The Jaguar is the biggest.
Kangaroo: Marsupials.
Kiwi: The Kiwi cannot fly.
Koala: False.
Kookaburra: Laughing Jackass.
Lemur: Madagascar.
Leopard: Up a tree.
Lion: False.
Llama: Guanaco.
Locust: Grasshoppers.
Loris: Primates.
Lynx: False. It is a cat.
Macaw: South America.
Mandrill: Forest.
Marmoset: Marmosets do not have opposable thumbs.
Meerkat: False.
Mongoose: Mongooses not Mongeese.
Monkey: Africa.
Muskox: They form a defensive circle, with bulls on the outside.
Ocelot: Because they have been hunted for their fur.
Okapi: Giraffe.
Orang-utan: 'Old Man of the Forest'.
Oryx: Saudi Arabia.
Ostrich: True.
Otter: True.
Owl: No.
Panda: Bamboo.
Penguin: One.
Piranha: True.
Porcupine: True.
Possum: Prehensile.
Praying Mantis: Because its front legs look as though they are held in prayer.
Python: True.
Reindeer: Caribou.
Rhea: False. Rheas can not fly.
Rhinoceros: Hair-like material.
Seahorse: False. Seahorses are fishes.
Sealion: True.
Serval: One. Servals usually live alone.
Shark: Cartilage.
Snake: To warn enemies that they might be posionous or to copy poisonous snakes and appear to be dangerous.
Spider: America.
Swan: Australia.
Tamarin: Because of its golden colour and the silky mane of hair covering its head and shoulders.
Tapir: True.
Terrapin: Reptile.
Tiger: False.
Toucan: Mainly fruit.
Vicuna: Llama.
Wolf: The Dog family.
Zebra: No one knows for certain.

ISBN 1 85671 126 9

Michelin Tyre Public Limited Company
Edward Hyde Building, 38 Clarendon Road, Watford, Herts WD1 1SX

A CIP record for this title is available from the British Library.

Edited and designed by Curtis Garratt Limited, The Old Vicarage, Horton cum Studley, Oxford OX9 1BT

The Publisher gratefully acknowledges the contribution of London Zoo who provided all the photographs in this I-Spy book. Cover photograph: Planet Earth Pictures. Title page photograph: Zoo Operations Ltd.

Colour reproduction by Norwich Litho Services Limited.

Printed in Spain.